GarethGates
What My Heart Wants To Sa

GW00656555

clusive distributors:
usic Sales Limited
Frith Street, London W1D 3JB, England.
usic Sales Pty Limited
0 Rothschild Avenue, Rosebery, NSW 2018, Australia.

der No. AM976349
3N 0-7119-9809-4
s book © Copyright 2002 by Wise Publications.

authorised reproduction of any part of this
blication by any means including photocopying
an infringement of copyright.

sic arrangements by Roger Day.
sic processed by Paul Ewers Music Design.
ide photographs courtesy of LFI.

nted in the United Kingdom by
igraving Limited, Thetford, Norfolk.

w.musicsales.com

r Guarantee of Quality:

publishers, we strive to produce every book
he highest commercial standards.

le endeavouring to retain the original running
er of the recorded album, the book has been
efully designed to minimise awkward page turns
to make playing from it a real pleasure.

ticular care has been given to specifying
l-free, neutral-sized paper made from pulps which
e not been elemental chlorine bleached.

pulp is from farmed sustainable forests and
produced with special regard for the environment.

ughout, the printing and binding have been
ned to ensure a sturdy, attractive publication
ch should give years of enjoyment.

ur copy fails to meet our high standards,
se inform us and we will gladly replace it.

publication is not authorised for sale
e United States of America and/or Canada

se Publications
ndon / New York / Paris / Sydney / Copenhagen / Berlin / Madrid / Tokyo

Unchained Melody

Words by Hy Zaret.
Music by Alex North.

© Copyright 1954 (renewed 1982) Frank Music Corporation, USA.
MPL Communications Limited.
All Rights Reserved. International Copyright Secured.

5

Anyone Of Us (Stupid Mistake)

Words & Music by Jörgen Elofsson, Per Magnusson & David Kreuger.

1. I've been let-ting you down, down. Girl, I know I've been such a fool._
(Verse 2 see block lyric)

Giv-ing in to temp - ta - tion,_ I should-'ve played it cool.

© Copyright 2002 BMG Music Publishing Limited (50%)/
Good Ear Music/Peermusic (UK) Limited (25%)/Warner/Chappell Music Limited (25%).
All Rights Reserved. International Copyright Secured.

no - thing to me, no - thing to me, swear ev - 'ry word_ is true.

Don't wan-na lose you._____ The si - tu - a - tion got

out of hand,_ I hope you un - der - stand. It can hap - pen to

a - ny - one of us, a - ny - one you think_ of. A - ny - one can fall,

Verse 2:
She was kind of exciting
A little crazy, I should've known
She must have altered my senses
'Cause I offered to walk her home.
The situation got out of hand
I hope you understand.

It can happen to any one of us *etc.*

Suspicious Minds

Words & Music by Francis Zambon.

© Copyright 1969 Sony/ATV Songs LLC, USA.
Sony/ATV Music Publishing (UK) Limited.
All Rights Reserved. International Copyright Secured.

18

C D Em Bm7
(With sus - pi - cious minds.)
and we can't build our dreams
C G/D D Bsus4 B
To Coda
1.
2.
2fr
on sus - pi - cious minds.
minds.
♩. = 54
Em Bm7 C D
Oh let our love sur - vive, or dry the tears from your eyes,
Em Bm7 C D
let's not let a good thing die, when you know I nev - er lied

Verse 2:
So if an old friend I know
Drops by to say hello
Would I still see suspicion in your eyes?

Here we go again
Asking where I've been
You can see these tears are real I'm crying

We can't go on together*etc.*

19

Downtown

Words & Music by Tommy Danvers & Tom Nichols.

© Copyright 2002 Sony/ATV Music Publishing (UK) Limited (50%)/
Universal Music Publishing Limited (50%).
All Rights Reserved. International Copyright Secured.

Now ba - by if___ you dance my way down town,_____ lit - tle skin on skin___ sure can___ be found.___ May - be you___ are all___ a - lone, can't do it on___ your own,_____ I'll show you hea - ven at___ the speed of sound.___

1.

Now ba - by if___ you come, come on, come___ on, come___ on down___

D.%. al Coda

Coda

Repeat ad lib. to fade

bo - dy pleads___ to feel the way_ it feels___ just trust me more_ than a - ny heart_ you saw,_ I'll give you all_ the love_ you're wait - ing for._____ Now ba - by if___ you

Verse 2:
Is the temperature hot enough for you to play?
Is it making your dreams suggest things you can't say?
If you'd ask me one time, two time, anytime that you like,
Got the perfect way to alleviate your stress tonight.

25

Sentimental

Words & Music by Graeme Kaerns, Mike Peden,
Ed Johnson & Gareth Gates.

© Copyright 2002 Global Talent Publishing
Sony/ATV Music Publishing (UK) Limited (25%)/
19 Songs Limited/BMG Music Publishing Limited (32.5%)/Copyright Control (42.5%).
All Rights Reserved. International Copyright Secured.

Em7

1. Girl, I don't be - lieve_ them when_ they tell___ me you_ don't love_ me,
(Verse 2 see block lyric)

F#7   Bm

some - times you seem_ to   think so lit - tle of___ me.

Em7

Ev - 'ry - bo - dy tells_ me that_ they see___ what's go - ing on.___

F#7   Bm

So quick to cri - ti - cise_ that what we have is wrong. I see you with an-

27

-oth - er_____ and I don't__ know what_ to do,__ 'cause the

prob - lem is_____ that I love__ you, yeah. I get sen - ti - men -

- tal, ba - by please be gen - tle.

Ba - by please, put my mind_ at ease,__ I get sen - ti - men -

a tempo 1°

Verse 2:
You make me unstable
But I like it
Never knowing where I stand
But I hide it.
The games that you're playing and things that you're saying
I really need to know
You got me completely, I've fallen so deeply
So please don't let me go.

What My Heart Wants To Say

Words & Music by Steve Mac & Jörgen Elofsson.

© Copyright 2002 Rokstone Music (50%)/BMG Music Publishing Limited (50%).
All Rights Reserved. International Copyright Secured.

But if I'll be gone to-mor-row, would you know how deep my love goes? Have I ev-er told you you're the one? If the words don't come my way, I hope you still know, I hope it still shows. If the words don't come my way, I hope you still

know what my heart___ wants to say.___ A love so

ten - der, I sur - ren - der to this feel - ing so___

true.___ My af - fir - ma - tion, my in - spi -

-ra - tion,___ dar - ling I have been blessed___ with you.___ If the

33

Good Thing

Words & Music by Steve Mac, Wayne Hector & Chris Laws.

1. I was look-ing for a new di-rec-tion, you got-ta keep mov-ing for your
(Verse 2 see block lyric)

© Copyright 2002 Rokstone Music (33.34%) / Rondor Music (London) Limited (33.33%) /
Damani Songs / Windswept Music (London) Limited (33.33%).
All Rights Reserved. International Copyright Secured.

Girl, you got me burn - ing up,— got me burn - ing, burn - ing up,— and I don't know how to stop,—

R.H. tacet 1°

__ got me burn - ing, burn - ing up._____ Girl you got me burn - ing up,__ got me burn - ing, burn - ing up,__

D.% *repeat Chorus to finish*

__ and I don't know how to stop,__ burn - ing up,_____ burn - ing up__

Verse 2:

I'm kinda warming to this new sensation,

'Cause every day is like a revelation.

Just show me something I never knew about me, yeah.

My friends can't lead me into no temptation,

'Cause baby you'll give me everything I'll ever need.

Fooling you makes a fool out of me.

(There's not a chance I'll take

'Cause I will never have to fake it with you.)

To Chorus

D.%

Love's the fuel in my fire, and it's taking us high

I'm not scared of desire, it's a good thing.

To Chorus

Too Serious Too Soon

Words & Music by Jörgen Elofsson, Per Magnusson & David Kreuger.

© Copyright 2002 BMG Music Publishing Limited (75%)/
Good Ear Music/Peermusic (UK) Limited (12.5%)/Warner/Chappell Music Limited (12.5%).
All Rights Reserved. International Copyright Secured.

Verse 2:
I told you every day
I told you every night in every way
I love you.
Maybe you got scared
That maybe I had nothing else to say
But I love you.

So baby now my life's a mess
'Cause I couldn't love you any less.

It Ain't Obvious

Words & Music by Mike Peden, Lucy Silvas & Cheryl Parker.

© Copyright 2002 19 Songs Limited/BMG Music Publishing Limited (33.33%)/Chrysalis Music Limited (66.67%).
All Rights Reserved. International Copyright Secured.

but it ain't ob - vi - ous.　　Why can't you just let it be?　　What would you have me be - lieve?

To Coda ⊕ | 1.

N.C.

I'm sure you real - ly want me,　　but it ain't ob - vi - ous.　　2. Why

2.

But it ain't ob - vi - ous,　　but it ain't ob - vi - ous,　　but it ain't ob - vi - ous,

but it ain't ob - vi - ous.　　Come on, won't you be with me,

50

Verse 2:
Why don't you put a little trust in me
And let it go?
If you don't take a chance
How will you ever know, baby I'm on your side.

Have I been foolish all along?
Have you been leading me on?
Just walk away
If this ain't where you belong.

With You All The Time

Words & Music by Jörgen Elofsson.

1. I live be-neath the heart,__ I watch you from__ the dark.__ I'm

(time.) *(Verse 2 see block lyric)*

ev-'ry breath,__ I'm ev-'ry dream,_____ I've known you for-

© Copyright 2002 BMG Music Publishing Limited.
All Rights Reserved. International Copyright Secured.

-ev - er, I've fol - lowed___ you ev -'ry - where. I'm ev -'ry star,___ I'm who you are._____

When you think you're a - lone, when you cry___ 'cause the world's un - fair,___ you can

rest as - sured_____ I'm al - ways there.___

Ev - en when you feel like you don't be - long, ev - en when you fall and it all goes

54

Save a lit - tle love for me___ and you'll see. Save a lit - tle love for me__

and you'll see, and you'll___ see.

___ Ev - en when you feel like you don't be - long, ev - en when you fall and it all goes
(2° ad lib.)

wrong. Know that I'm with___ you, I'm with you all the time.

56

Verse 2:
I walk your every road
I'm laughing when you smile
And when you cry, I cry too.
I made you a promise
That I shall forever keep
You're on your own
But not alone.

When you're down, when you're out
When the world tells you no one cares
You can rest assured
I'm always there.

(I've Got No) Self Control

Words & Music by Jewels & Stone & Rob Davis.

© Copyright 2002 19 Song Limited/BMG Music Publishing Limited (50%)/Universal Music Publishing Limited (50%).
All Rights Reserved. International Copyright Secured.

59

You're mak-ing me hot,___ you're mak-ing me sweat.___

I've got___ no,___ no self con-trol___ when I'm with___ you. Oh___ what I'll give___ you ba-by.

I've got___ no,___ no self con-trol___ when I'm 'round___ you, I'm los-ing it all___ for___ you.___

___ La la la la la___ la la.___ La la la la la___ la la.___ 2. I'm un-der

2.

I'm out of my mind,___ I'm out-ta my head,___ I'm los-ing my heart,___

la la.

I'm ea-si-ly led.___ Like noth-ing be-fore,___ as good as it gets,___

you're mak-ing me hot,___ you're mak-ing me sweat.___

N.C.

D.%. al Coda

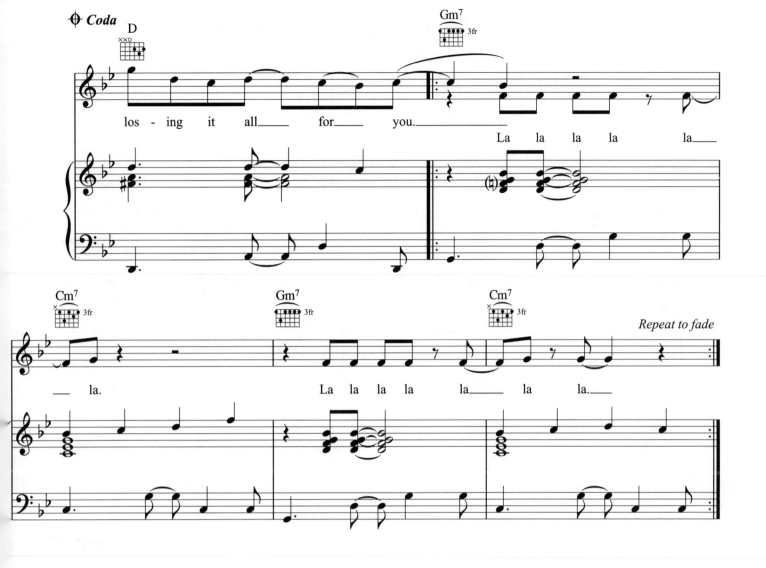

los - ing it all___ for___ you.___ La la la la la___

___ la. La la la la la___ la la.___

Repeat to fade

Verse 2:
I'm under no illusion
I'm in such confusion
I can't help myself.
I think I need protection
From a deep affection
Don't want nobody else.

I'm falling apart
I want you to know
The more you resist
The deeper I go
The longer I wait
The weaker I get
You're making me hot
You're making me sweat.

Tell Me One More Time

Words & Music by Oskar Paul, Cathy Dennis & Andrew Fromm.

© Copyright 2002 Sony/ATV Music Publishing (UK) Limited (27%)/EMI Music Publishing Limited (40%)/
Ocean At Night Music/Zomba Music Publishers Limited (33%).
All Rights Reserved. International Copyright Secured.

Mm.___ And when___ you find the one___ wher-

-ev - er you go___ they'll tra - vel with you?___

What can I say?___ Where do I start___ to pick up the pie - ces of

your bro - ken heart?___

65

won't be - lieve___ it's true___ un - til I hear it from you.___

Back in my life, I want you so bad,___ and los - ing you is los - ing

all that I had.___ And this is cra - zy, so why can't you see___

Verse 2:
Do you believe in love?
There's no right, no wrong, no, no
Love's just an open road
With different ways of moving on.
I dare you to stay
And work this thing out
'Cause leaving is taking
The easy way out.

Alive

Words & Music by Tom Nichols, Andrew Todd & James Graydon.

Da da da da da da da, da da da da da da da

da. Da da da da da da da,

da da da da da da da. Da da da.

© Copyright 2002 Good Groove Songs Limited/Universal Music Publishing Limited (33.34%)/
BMG Music Publishing Limited (33.33%)/Copyright Control (33.33%)
All Rights Reserved. International Copyright Secured.

Verse 2:
You know why he wants you
But I ain't the same as him
I look a little further within.
Your life has had some long nights
All those tears I wipe away
Just close your eyes and hear what I say.

One And Ever Love

Words & Music by Simon Franglen & Angela Lupino.

1. It's cold out-side, so un-der-stand__ if I don't hang a-round__ to wave.__ I'll say good-bye__

(Verse 2 see block lyric)

__ and kiss__ your hand__ and then get on with be-ing brave.__ But don't ex -

© Copyright 2000 EMI Music Publishing Limited.
All Rights Reserved. International Copyright Secured.

76

some day you might learn a - gain,___ it's you I'm dream - ing of. And

mean - while I'll be here,___ and I'll pray to God___ a - bove___

___ that some day you might turn___ a - gain___ to me,___ your

one and ev - er love. 2. It's cold out - one and ev - er, one and ev - er.

78

that some day you might turn a - gain to me,

your one and ev - er love.

Verse 2:
It's cold outside, so understand
If I don't hang around and cry
I'll let you go without a word
And then be bluer than the sky.

And I'll try not to watch you go
And I'll try not to stand alone.
Behind you in the snow
Behind you in the sky.

Walk On By

Words & Music by Jörgen Elofsson & David Kreuger.

1. I'm com-ing down with a heart-ache to-night,_ on-ly you__ can make__ it__ right._
(Verse 2 see block lyric)

____ If I can't be with you hold-ing you tight,_ there won't be_

© Copyright 1999 BMG Music Publishing Limited (60%)/Zomba Music Publishers Limited (40%).
All Rights Reserved. International Copyright Secured.

Verse 2:

I keep my cool, I pretend I'm not here
Every time you come too near.
I'm such a fool 'cause this love is real
And if I don't tell you, someone else surely will.

That's When You Know

Words & Music by Peter Gordeno, Howard New & Mike Peden.

1. For ev-'ry-one the sto-ry goes, there's a spe-cial some-one to make them whole. Some-one to give_ their heart com-plete - ly.

© Copyright 2002 19 Songs Limited/BMG Music Publishing Limited (25%)/
Kobalt Music Publishing Limited (50%)/Copyright control (25%).
All Rights Reserved. International Copyright Secured.

Verse 2:
And who can tell the time and place
When you see your soul reflected in their face.
It would be a spell you're under
And it'll hit you just like thunder.